THE 5TH COMIC BOOK

I ALSO WANT GOOD 'THEORY OF MIND'

THE GIRL WITH THE CURLY HAIR
HELPING PEOPLE WITH ASPERGER'S SYNDROME AND THEIR LOVED ONES COMMUNICATE
BY ALIS ROWE

Also by Alis Rowe

One Lonely Mind
978-0-9562693-0-0

The Girl with the Curly Hair - Asperger's and Me
978-0-9562693-2-4

The 1st Comic Book
978-0-9562693-1-7

The 2nd Comic Book
978-0-9562693-4-8

The 3rd Comic Book
978-0-9562693-3-1

The 4th Comic Book
978-1-5086839-7-1

Websites:
www.alisrowe.co.uk
www.thegirlwiththecurlyhair.co.uk
www.womensweightlifting.co.uk

Social Media:
www.facebook.com/thegirlwiththecurlyhair
www.twitter.com/curlyhairedalis

The Girl with the Curly Hair

presents

The 5th Comic Book

Alis Rowe

Lonely Mind Books
London

Copyrighted Material

First published in 2016
by Lonely Mind Books
London

Copyright © Alis Rowe 2016

All rights reserved. No part of this publication may be reproduced in any material form (including photocopying or storing it in any medium by electronic means and whether or not transiently or incidentally to some other use of this publication) without written permission of the copyright owner except in accordance with the provisions of the Copyright, Designs and Patents Act 1988 or under the terms of a licence issued by the Copyright Licensing Agency Ltd, 90 Tottenham Court Road, London, England W1T 4LP. Applications for the copyright owner's written permission to reproduce any part of this publication should be addressed to the publisher.

Warning: The doing of an unauthorised act in relation to a copyright work may result in both a civil claim for damages and criminal prosecution.

ISBN 9781530987931

For anyone who wants to relate to somebody with ASD

and

my Facebook friends

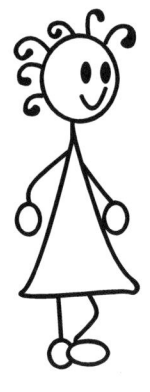

hello

'Theory of mind' is the term used to explain how different people have different thoughts, views and plans. In the simplest sense, it means recognising that what's in somebody else's head is not the same as what's in yours!

It is a topic that has always fascinated me and I believe that all people, whether on the spectrum or not, can develop their theory of mind.

You will notice that some of these comic strips demonstrate that even neurotypicals can have weak theory of mind in relation to the person with ASD. For each comic strip, see if you can work out which character has the impaired theory of mind and is struggling to see the other's point of view!

I think that developing one's theory of mind is a key component to building any successful relationship - but particularly with a person on the autism spectrum.

I hope this book opens your mind to another's!

Best wishes,

Alis aka The Girl with the Curly Hair

Contents

Row a boat	11
Head bump	15
Hungry?	19
Building blocks	23
Fire alarm	27
21st	31
Green peppers	35
Going to the gym	39
A trip out	43
Planets	47
'The Full Uni Experience'	51
Playdate	55
Taking the bin out	59
Mum goes away	63
A taxing text	67
Cinema and pizza	71
Meeting a friend	75
You're not listening	79
Dad's on the phone	83
Blinds	87
Made redundant	91

Row a boat

Space for your notes...

THE GIRL WITH THE CURLY HAIR

HAS BEEN INVITED BY A FRIEND TO ROW A BOAT DOWN THE RIVER WITH FRIENDS.

SHE POLITELY SAYS NO BUT HER FRIEND ONLY SEES IT FROM HER OWN POINT OF VIEW.

> MY IDEA OF A NIGHTMARE. I DO NOT ENJOY SOCIAL CHIT CHAT, I HATE HOT WEATHER, I DON'T LIKE BEING AROUND LOTS OF PEOPLE...

> I JUST CAN'T UNDERSTAND IT! WHY DOESN'T SHE WANT TO COME? IT'S GOING TO BE SO FUN!

> ...I'LL BE OUT OF ROUTINE. USUALLY AT WEEKENDS I LIKE BEING BY MYSELF AND DOING WEIGHTLIFTING

> I AM HOWEVER, VERY GLAD THAT SHE INVITED ME. IT MAKES ME FEEL INCLUDED

> IT'LL BE A HOT, SUNNY DAY, LOTS OF FRIENDS TOGETHER, A RELAXING RIDE DOWN THE BEAUTIFUL RIVER...

Head bump

Space for your notes...

The Girl with the Curly Hair

bumps her head. Her Mum was not there. Even so, she assumes her Mum knows what has happened.

Oh no, I was in a bad mood already and now I've hit my head. It hurts!

Why aren't you helping me? You don't care that I've hurt myself!

What on earth has happened, love?

How can she not know I bumped my head and hurt myself?

I wasn't even in the room, I'm not sure what's going on

Hungry

Space for your notes...

The Girl with the Curly Hair

is waiting for dinner to be served. **Her mum** said it would be ready at 7.30pm. Her need to stick to routine and timings is misunderstood as impatience.

> I feel agitated, dinner is not ready

> She said 7.30pm. I go to bed at 8.00pm. I feel anxious, I will be late getting to bed

> Mum, is dinner ready yet? It's 7.31pm

> She's so impatient. I feel so rushed

> Please stop going on and on and on, it'll be ready soon!

> If you're hungry, go and get yourself a snack

> I am not hungry, I already had a snack to prepare for this late meal. I feel out of routine and stressed

Building blocks

Space for your notes...

The Girl with the Curly Hair
AND HER FRIEND ARE PLAYING WITH BUILDING BLOCKS. SHE MODIFIES HER FRIEND'S HOUSE.
SHE NEEDED MORE SPACE... SO SHE MADE MORE SPACE.

Girl (thought): I HAVE MUCH MORE SPACE TO BUILD NOW!

Girl: I'M BUILDING A SWIMMING POOL. IT'S GOING TO BE AWESOME!

Friend: WHAT ARE YOU DOING?! I WAS IN THE MIDDLE OF BUILDING THAT

Friend (thought): SHE'S SO RUDE TOUCHING MY STUFF. I DON'T WANT TO PLAY WITH HER ANYMORE

Fire alarm

Space for your notes...

The Girl with the Curly Hair
is in a lesson, when the fire alarm goes off. They always have fire drills on Fridays at 10am.

Is there a fire? I am very frightened

I love all these practice fire alarms, it's a way to get out of boring lessons!

It's great chatting to my friends in the playground

The noise is so loud, it's hurting my ears!

I was in the middle of writing, I feel cross that I have to stop

"Yay, come on, let's go and play outside. This is such fun!"

21st

Space for your notes...

The Girl with the Curly Hair is nearly 21. Her friend is planning a party for her.
Her friend assumes she'll enjoy a big party, like everyone else!

Girl: My favourite way to spend the day is at home with my cats, reading a book, and doing weightlifting

Friend: She's just worried about all the organising! She'll be fine once it's organised

Girl: I just want to do my normal activities

Friend: But it's your 21st! It's important to do something special!

Friend: Let's have a big party and invite everyone from uni!

Girl: Now I just feel really, really stressed

Green peppers

Space for your notes...

The Girl with the Curly Hair
is cutting up some peppers so that the little boy she is looking after can have a healthy snack.
She does not check what he likes.

Peppers are delicious, apart from the green ones, I don't like those. So I won't give him the green one, just red and orange

Here are some peppers for you

Thanks! Are there any green ones? They're my favourite

But how can he like the green ones? They are horrible! I'm confused

Going to the gym

SPACE FOR YOUR NOTES...

The Girl with the Curly Hair

asks *her neurotypical partner* whether he has been to the gym today.
She loves the gym.

Him: I don't like going to the gym, it's just another chore. I hate exercise...

Her: It's very important to do some sort of exercise every day. I want him to keep healthy

Him: ...I only do it because I know it's good for me

Him: No, not today. I didn't feel like it

Him: I just wanted to have a day off! It's fine to have a day off...

Him: I wish she wouldn't ask me every single day, it makes me feel bad

Her: I don't understand! How could he not have felt like it? Going to the gym is amazing, it's my favourite thing in the world

A trip out

Space for your notes...

The Girl with the Curly Hair
and her sister are planning a trip out.
It's Sunday and they always go to the park.

Curly Hair Girl (speech): Let's go to the park!

Sister (thought): We always go to the park, it's so boring! I want to do something different

Sister (speech): I don't want to go to the park again, I want to go bowling!

Curly Hair Girl (thought): But we always go to the park, why does she want to change? I don't understand, I feel unsettled and confused

Planets

Space for your notes...

The Girl with the Curly Hair
is in science class. The teacher announces that today they are going to learn the names of the planets.
It just does not occur to her that the other pupils might not know what she knows.

> But I already know the names of all the planets. Can't we do something else?

> You're not the only member of this class! What about everybody else? I'm sure they will want to know

> They don't know? But I know, why don't they? I'm confused

'The Full Uni Experience'

Space for your notes...

The Girl with the Curly Hair
is applying to a small, local university.
She knows exactly what she wants but her peers and teachers don't seem to be listening.

> It's really important that you move away and live away from home to get the full uni experience!

> If you don't live on campus, you'll be missing out on so much

> You'll find it extremely difficult to make friends if you don't live on campus

> Why on earth are you applying there?!

> She's so bright, she should be going to Oxbridge

> Why do they keep saying these things? I've already told them that I want to stay at home

Playdate

Space for your notes...

The Girl with the Curly Hair

had a friend round on Sunday. On Monday, her dad asks her if they played again at school. She does not see any connection between a weekend playdate at home and playtime at school.

Dad: Did you say hello to Sarah today? Did you play with her again?

Girl: No. No.

Dad (thinking): But they had such a great time yesterday... Why does she always blank her friends? She's never going to have any friends if she always blanks them. I wonder if I should explain to Sarah's mum.

Taking the bin out

Space for your notes...

The Girl with the Curly Hair
IS WORKING IN THE STUDY. **Her Dad** WALKS PAST HER TO GO OUTSIDE, CARRYING THE BIN BAG. *He was running late for work.*

Why didn't he go the other way? He didn't need to pass me. He knows I can't stand the smell of B.I.N.S.

"I don't like the smell of that, it makes me feel sick"

"Oh, I'm sorry"

Oh dear, she is right. I know she doesn't like it. I didn't think. I should have gone the other way

Mum goes away

Space for your notes...

The Girl with the Curly Hair
is saying "goodbye" to her Mum, who is going on holiday for a week.
She doesn't like being away from home, so assumes her mum doesn't either.

Mummy, are you going to be OK? You will feel lonely and sad away from home

Of course! I'm really looking forward to a nice little break. I'll definitely miss you but I'll be home again soon!

I would feel lonely and sad if I went away

Lonely and sad? It's sweet she worries but lonely and sad are the last things I'll feel!

A taxing text

The Girl with the Curly Hair
receives a text message from *her neurotypical partner* at 6pm.
Routines are more important than relationships.

> **<Hey, my mum just text me and wants me to help her with her tax return tonight. Can I see you tomorrow night instead?>**

He can see her in the daytime. He has to be in with me tonight because that's what we always do. I feel anxious

We always see each other every night, he is making a big change, I feel stressed

Cinema and pizza

Space for your notes...

The Girl with the Curly Hair

and her neurotypical partner have just seen a film at the cinema. They have different experiences of spontaneity.

Neurotypical partner: "I'm starving!"

Neurotypical partner: "That was great! Let's go for pizza now, I want to treat you!"

Girl with curly hair: "Tired now. Film was good but I want to go home and get back to my routine. Feeling overwhelmed"

Girl with curly hair: "No thank you, I want to go home now"

Neurotypical partner: "She loves pizza, she'll love it when she's eating it. She just needs a bit of persuasion"

Girl with curly hair: "We had not planned to eat out, I had planned my normal lunch routine. I feel stressed"

Meeting a friend

Space for your notes...

The Girl with the Curly Hair
has arranged to meet her neurotypical friend.
She had planned exactly what they would talk about.

Neurotypical friend: Hope you don't mind! I bumped into Rachel on the way so I invited her along!

Curly Hair: What is Rachel doing with her? I had not planned to see Rachel. I feel nervous

Curly Hair: Socialising with more than one person is stressful and difficult, I find it hard to join in the conversation and I always feel left out

Neurotypical friend: She likes Rachel, it'll be great to all catch up together

Curly Hair: I planned what I would say to Anna but I didn't plan what I would say to Rachel. I feel very anxious

You're not listening

Space for your notes...

The Girl with the Curly Hair
is in a lesson at school. **The teacher** comes to her desk and starts talking to her.
She can't look and listen at the same time.

Teacher: She's not looking at me, that means she's not listening

Teacher: Please look at me when I'm talking to you

Girl: I won't understand what he is saying if I look at him at the same time

Girl: I don't understand why I have to look at him. I am listening very hard, even if I'm not looking

Dad's on the phone

Space for your notes...

The Girl with the Curly Hair
is talking to her Dad on the phone. He asks her what she is doing.
She holds up her toys as she speaks.

- Playing with this
- My toy lions
- What are you playing with, love? I can't see!

Blinds

SPACE FOR YOUR NOTES...

The Girl with the Curly Hair

and her colleagues have just arrived at work. It is a bright, sunny day. The intensity of the light is very painful for her.

Oh, what a glorious day! Let's open the blinds!

What a horrible day, the bright light is hurting my eyes. It's giving me a headache

I don't want to open the blinds. I want the blinds to stay closed. I feel very uncomfortable

This weather is so nice! We better make the most of it

How do I tell them that the light hurts my eyes? I don't know what to say. I'm worried they'll just laugh at me

Made redundant

Space for your notes...

The Girl with the Curly Hair

has a visit from her neurotypical partner after he has finished work. He tells her that he's been made redundant. He's really worried about how he'll pay his rent.

Girl: Excellent, he can be at home with me tomorrow. I'm so happy

Partner: I feel worthless and miserable

Partner: All I can think about now is finding a new job

Girl: Does that mean you will be able to help me do weightlifting tomorrow?

Partner: Is that really all she cares about? She doesn't care how I feel

The end

Index

Sensory
Fire alarm	27
Taking the bin out	59
Cinema and pizza	71
You're not listening	79
Blinds	87

Relationships
Going to the gym	39
A taxing text	67
Cinema and pizza	71
Made redundant	91

Socialising
Row a boat	11
Building blocks	23
Fire alarm	27
21st	31
'The Full Uni Experience'	51
Playdate	55
Meeting a friend	75

Rigid thinking
Head bump	15
Green peppers	35
Playdate	55

Routine
Row a boat	11
Hungry	19
21st	31
A trip out	43
A taxing text	67
Cinema and pizza	71

Taking things literally
Hungry	19

Anxiety
Hungry	19
Mum goes away	63
Meeting a friend	75

Special interests
Row a boat	11
21st	31
Going to the gym	39
Made redundant	91

Change
Row a boat	11
Fire alarm	27
A trip out	43
A taxing text	67

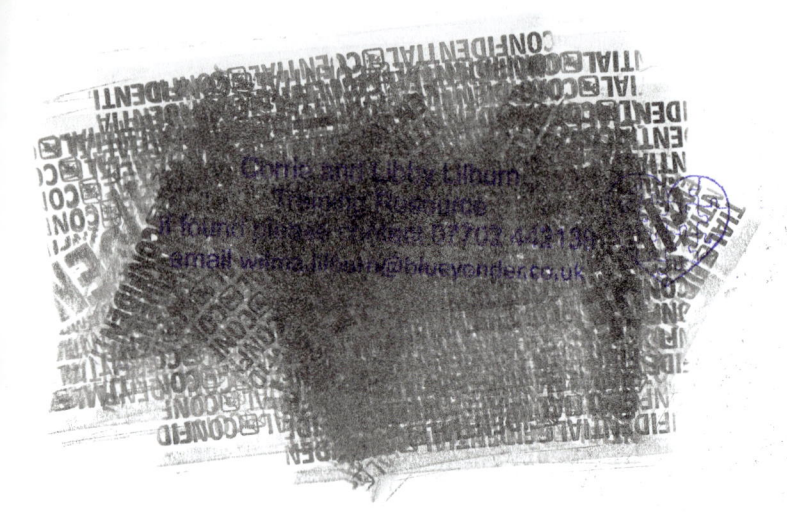

Printed in Great Britain
by Amazon